Cats You're Going to Love!

Going to School

Cats You're Going to Love!

Going to School

Suzanne Green

PERLORIAN KITTEN SCHOOL

Willowisp Press®

First published in this edition in 1990
by Willowisp Press, Inc.
10100 SBF Drive, Pinellas Park, Florida 34666

Published by arrangement with Doubleday, a division of Bantam,
Doubleday, Dell Publishing Group, Inc.

Perlorian Cats is a trademark of Satoru Tsuda

Library of Congress Cataloging-in-Publication Data
Green, Suzanne.
   Going to school.
   Summary: Young cats prepare for school and enjoy the regular
activities of the school day, from art class and recess to naptime
and a spelling bee.
   [1.Cats—Fiction. 2. Schools—Fiction] I. Title
PZ7.G82634Go   1987   [E]   86-32819

Printed in the United States of America

10 9 8 7 6 5 4 3 2

ISBN 0-87406-481-3

Note to Grown-ups

The "Perlorian Cats" that you see here are very special animals photographed by a very caring group of photographers led by Satoru Tsuda. The cats are specially chosen for their expressive faces and comfort with the photography sessions.

These photographs are taken at incredibly high shutter speeds to capture a pose and an expression without any discomfort to the cat or cats involved. No artificial substances are used—just love and patience! And the cats seem to respond beautifully to the attention and caring that surround them.

Needless to say, no one should try to do this with cats or kittens on their own. Professional training and proper circumstances should always be involved when working with animals. Your family cat will not welcome treatment it is not used to. Cats are very independent animals!

What will I wear to school tomorrow?

It's so hard to decide!

Off I go to sleep.

Good morning, chicks. I'm going to school today.

First I brush my teeth.

Then I get dressed.

Mother has made me a big breakfast . . .

and packed me a nice lunch
to take.

Here's the bus!

I play with my friend before
the bell rings.

My first class is fun.

My friend and I are
building a house with
blocks.

I feel very creative today in art class.

Now we sing songs.

I love recess!

Lunchtime and I'm hungry.

And now we take a nap
together.

My friends and I are in a
spelling bee.

Now we say good-bye for today.

It's time to go home.

Mother comes to the bus to
pick me up.

I love telling my parents
about my day in school.

Boy, am I tired!

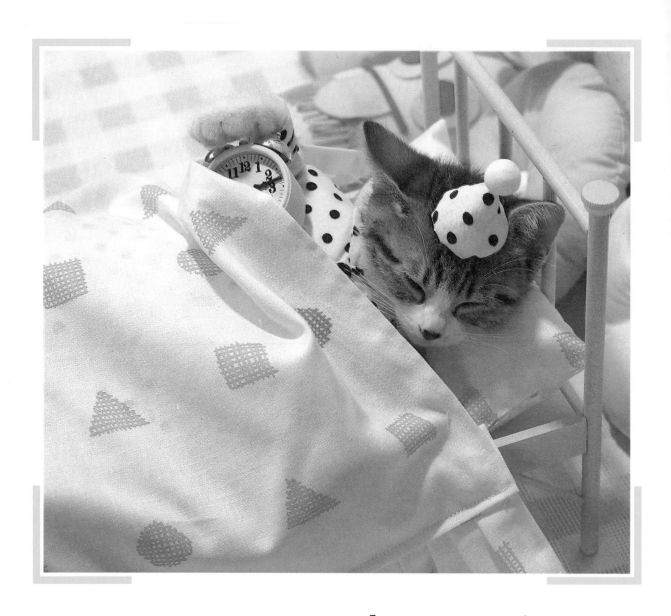

I can't wait until tomorrow!